The Emperor's New Clothes

A Comedy in Three Acts

to be played by or for Children

By

CHARLOTTE CHORPENNING

SAMUEL FRENCH

Founded 1845 . Incorporated 1899

25 West 45th St.
New York City

811 West 7th St.
Los Angeles

Snow White and the Seven Dwarfs

by JESSIE BRAHAM WHITE

FANTASY—3 ACTS

24 Characters—Scenes: the Palace, the Witch's Hut, the Dwarfs' Home, the Forest

The handsome version of the famous fairy tale as presented in New York by Winthrop Ames. Supposedly disposed of by the wicked queen, Snow White finds her way to a happy glen and the home of seven friendly dwarfs. A deadly apple casts her into a deep sleep, from which she is revived in time by her devoted prince.

(*Royalty,* $25-$20.)

Beauty and the Beast

by JESSE BEERS, JR.

FANTASY—2 ACTS

10 Characters—One Setting, with 3 Hearths

Beauty is enamored with a handsome prince whom she saw in an apparition. Her love draws her to the nearby castle of the unspeakable Beast, which she enters unafraid. A magic mirror and many other magnificent gifts are given her by the Beast. But it is her final, fearless expression of affection for the Beast that breaks the spell on the Beast and returns him to the form of the handsome Prince. A very picturesque and moving version of the famous tale, with ingeniously simple staging.

(*Royalty,* $15.00.)

When ordering, state author's name.

The Emperor's New Clothes

A Play for Children in Three Acts

By
CHARLOTTE CHORPENNING

SAMUEL FRENCH
Founded 1845 . Incorporated 1899

25 WEST 45TH ST.
NEW YORK CITY

811 WEST 7TH ST.
LOS ANGELES

Press and bindery of The Conway Printing Co.
New York

THE EMPEROR'S NEW CLOTHES

CAST OF CHARACTERS

ZAR
ZAN
TSEIN
LING
MONG
FAH
THE GONG BOY
HAN
THE GENERAL
THE EMPEROR
THE EMPRESS
A CHILD
WEAVERS OF THE ROYAL STUFFS
CITIZENS

TIME: Long ago.
PLACE: A country much like China.

ACT I: *The Street of the Royal Weavers. The middle of the morning.*

ACT II: *A room in Han's quarters, in the palace. Noon, the next day.*

ACT III: *Same as* ACT I. *Afternoon of the same day.*

NOTE

This play was written for the Children's Theatre of Evanston, where it was played by university students to six audiences of from three to five hundred children each.

The success of this production has led to a variety of other performances. The play seems suited to any age from the fifth grade up. It has been played by two other adult groups for other children; by the children of the Chicago Civic Theatre on the Navy Pier, ranging from six to fifteen years of age; by a junior high school and a senior high school, with equal success.

It is easily adjusted to specific needs. Zar has been played by a woman with perfect satisfaction. All parts have been played by women. Music has been introduced twice, special music being written for the Gong Boy's chant and the Weaver's chant, for Han and the General as well as for the Emperor. If such talent is not available, however, Chinese records make satisfactory music for the Emperor. A fascinating variation was the substitution of the Emperor's dancing before his people, for his walking in procession. At the Navy Pier the cast was enlarged to use over two hundred children, by substituting a group of singing maidens for the Gong Boy, multiplying the numbers of the Weavers and Citizens, and using very small children in large numbers for the final, "The Emperor has on nothing but a shirt!"

The Emperor's New Clothes

ACT I

The Street of the Royal Weavers, in the EMPEROR'S *city. It should suggest China but need not be too literal. High on one of the buildings is the sign: The Street of the Royal Weavers.*

Enter ZAR *and* ZAN, *looking eagerly about. The important thing about them is that they are full of the zest for life, and are tingling for adventure. They belong to no particular country.*

ZAR

Everything is so quiet.

ZAN

This is the emperor's own city. It ought to be a good place for things to happen.

ZAR

(*Reading the sign.*) The Street of the Royal Weavers.

ZAN

This ought to be a good street for adventures. The Royal Weavers have gold, and jewels to work with.

ZAR

And bright threads! Green, like jade. And scarlet. And the color of the sky.

ZAN

And they think up strange things to weave!

ZAR

Trees that nobody ever saw! And white birds, like the ones you see in the clouds!

ZAN

And dragons!

ZAR

Oh, strange things could happen here!

ZAN

We have come to a fine place!

ZAR

But why is it so quiet?

ZAN

They can't be asleep. It's the middle of the morning.

ZAR

(*Pointing to the houses.*) I feel as if something exciting were happening in there.

ZAN

Listen, and find out. (*They run to put an ear to the door of one of the houses, but just as they do so a great gong sounds, off, making them leap high in the air with fright. A* GONG BOY *enters* [*or it could be a group of Chinese court maidens, if desired to use more girls*] *followed by* HAN, *the minister of the* EMPEROR'S *robes.* HAN *stalks by, ferocious, proud, looking neither to the right nor left, the gong being struck at every second or third step. The rogues leap to hide at first sight of them, peering from behind some corner.* HAN *crosses the stage and exits. The rogues steal out to gaze after him.*) What do you suppose that means?

ZAR

It makes me shiver.

ZAN

I don't like that man.

ZAR

I don't like his face.

ZAN

I don't like the way he walks.

ZAR

He wants people to be afraid of him.

(*Again the gong sounds, and sends them scurrying to hide. The* GONG BOY [*or the maidens*] *returns, halts center, and strikes the gong with a flourish.*)

GONG BOY

(*Chanting.*)
Weavers of cunning silks!
Bring out your wares!
Han passes by! (*Flourish on the gong.*)

Great Han passes by! (*Flourish.*)
He buys stuff for the emperor's new clothes!
One hundred and one robes the emperor needs
Before the April moon is old!
Bring out your wares!
Great Han will choose!
Bring out your shining silks!
(*Flourish and exit.*)

ZAN

The man's name is Han.

ZAR

He's coming here again!

ZAN

To buy cloth for the emperor's robes!

ZAR

How can he choose for the emperor's robes? He doesn't know what is beautiful!

ZAN

He doesn't care whether things are beautiful or not!

ZAR

He'll cheat the weavers!

ZAN

If he tries to cheat the weavers, we'll take their part!

ZAR

This will be the best adventure we've ever had!

ZAN

I wonder why the weavers don't bring out their stuff?

ZAR

I wonder if they heard the call. (*He crosses to listen at a door.*) Some one's crying.

ZAN

(*At another door.*) Some one's crying here.

(*The doors are suddenly pushed open, sending the rogues tumbling across the stage.* TSEIN *and* MONG *enter.*)

TSEIN

Aha! I heard you at my door!

MONG

That wicked Han sent you!

ROGUES

(*Together.*) Nobody sent us!

TSEIN

What were you doing at my door?

BOTH

We were looking for an adventure.

MONG

I'll give you an adventure! (*She runs about, beating on the doors.*) Ling! Fah! all of you! A spy! Another spy!

TSEIN

(*As crowd enters.*) They were listening at our doors!

CROWD

A spy! Han's men! Han sent them! (*Etc.*)

LING

Beat the coats off their backs!

CROWD

Beat them!

LING

The way Han's servants beat me, when I stuck to my price!

MONG

Starve them! The way Han is starving our children!

FAH

Bring some cord! Tie them up! Bring me a lash!

ZAN

We aren't Han's men!

ZAR

We don't like Han!

ZAN

We want to take your part against him!

TSEIN

What has he done to you?

ZAN

He hasn't done anything to us.

ZAR

We never heard of him till he went past just now.

FAH

Don't believe them! Every one knows Han!

MONG

Every one knows how he robs the people!

CROWD

Beat them! Lash them!

(*They raise their lashes, etc., but the* OLD WOMAN *checks them.*)

OLD WOMAN

Wait!—Why do you take our part against him if he has done nothing to you?

ZAR

We don't like his face.

ZAN

We don't like the way he walks.

FAH

Those are not reasons.

ZAN

Yes they are. We don't like people who do those things.

ZAR

That's why we want to take your part.

OLD WOMAN

Come here. (*They approach her fearfully. She fixes her piercing eye on their faces, probing their eyes.*) What they say is true. Untie their hands.

FAH

Put away the lash.

TSEIN

Who are you?

ZAN

His name is Zar.

ZAR

His name is Zan.

FAH

Where do you come from?

ZAR

From wherever we've had an adventure.

MONG

Where have you had adventures?

ZAN

In towered cities, and green fields.

ZAR

Beyond the mountains and across the seas.

TSEIN

What is your trade?

ZAR

Whatever we need to make things happen right.

MONG

There isn't any sense to that.

ZAN

Once we were sailors, because our plan needed ships.

ZAR

Once we carried a beggar's bowl because we needed to watch the faces of many men.

FAH

What will you do in our city?

ZAN

We don't know yet.

ZAR

Our plan hasn't come.

TSEIN

How can you take our part against Han?

ZAN

We don't know that yet, either.

MONG

You talk foolish talk.

ZAR

Do you know what flowers and dragons and birds you will weave into your next piece of cloth?

MONG

Of course not. Not till we start.

TSEIN

They are waiting in our fingers and our hearts.

ZAR

Our next adventure is waiting in us like that.

ZAN

Just trust us and we will take your part against Han!

LING

Aren't you afraid? Han is the richest man in the kingdom.

FAH

And the most powerful.

MONG

Even the emperor does what Han says. He thinks of nothing but his new clothes and believes whatever Han tells him.

TSEIN

It is a great risk to go against Han. He has spies everywhere.

LING

You see it is dangerous to take our part.

ZAR

If it were safe it wouldn't be an adventure!

ZAN

Have you any plan against Han now?

MANY

Yes.

TSEIN

We were praying to our ancestors for courage to carry it out.

ZAN

Tell us your plan.

(*The gong sounds off. Every one starts in terror.*)

TSEIN

He is coming! Listen, and you will hear our plan. (*The rogues run to hide. The weavers gather together, like a herd in danger.*) Who will speak for us?

FAH

I will speak!

MONG

No! You will be too angry. Han will have us all killed for what you say!

TSEIN

Let Ling speak. His tongue runs smooth.

(*Enter* HAN, *preceded by the* GONG BOY, *who stops with a flourish.*)

HAN

What is this? Did you not hear the boy, who told you I was coming?

FAH

We heard!!

(LING, *putting* FAH *aside and trying to smooth over his violence.*)

LING

We heard, great Han.

HAN

Then why is not your cloth spread out for me to see?

LING

You are very great, O Han. But it is in our minds to return to the way of our fathers.

HAN

Your fathers were weavers like yourselves.

LING

That is true, great Han. But our fathers, and their fathers before them, showed the stuff they wove to the emperor himself. From the emperor's hand they received the price of their work.

HAN

This is insolence! Bring out your cloth!

LING

When the emperor comes, O great and mighty Han.

HAN

The emperor has no time to be picking and choosing from many pieces of cloth! He must be dressed in splendor, and every hour in a new robe. Bring out your goods that I may choose for him before he comes! (*No one moves.*) How! (*The weavers crowd closer together, trembling but doggedly silent.*) My word is the same as the emperor's word! I can cast those who disobey me into a dungeon! I can have their heads struck off! Fetch it out! What are you waiting for?

LING

We wish to show it only to the emperor, O just and merciful Han.

HAN

The emperor will see what I show him, and nothing more!

FAH

(*Breaking out of the crowd.*) And you will show him only what we pay you to show him! And when we have put our price in gold into your hand, you will find fault with our weaving, and keep the best for yourself, pretending it is unfit! (*The weavers try to restrain him, but he breaks from them, shaking his fist in* HAN'S *face.*) You are a thief and a liar! You keep the costly gold the emperor sends for our weaving and give us make-believe gold! You keep the rare jewels and send us glass in their place! We will not pay you a penny! Our stuff is safe locked up in our houses! The price of it shall never touch your fingers!

(*The weavers try to hush him, more and more terrified as* HAN'S *anger mounts. Finally they hold him quiet.*)

HAN

(*Quiet but fierce.*) The emperor shall never see one thread of your work.

LING

When the emperor comes, Great Han ——

HAN

I will tell him that not a piece of it is fit for his eyes to rest on. You shall not sell the emperor one yard this whole year.

(*Murmurs from the crowd.*)

A BYSTANDER

(*Above it.*) How shall we live?

HAN

After the emperor has gone, I will send my servants into your houses to find out your stuff and tear it into tatters and cast it into the mud of the streets.

TSEIN

(*On her knees.*) No, no, Great Han! This time I have woven the most beautiful thing of my life. Do not destroy it!

HAN

Let me see it.

(TSEIN *struggles with herself. The weavers hang on her decision, anxious lest she give up.*)

TSEIN

(*Lifting her head resolutely.*) I am a weaver. Ling spoke for us all.

HAN

The emperor is on his way to your street, with his empress. I will go to prepare his mind. Be ready for his wrath.

(*Exit* HAN, *preceded by the* GONG BOY. *Weeping and despair among the weavers.*)

LING

Tsein! Bring out the most beautiful thing of your life. If it is here, the emperor's eye may rest on it.

TSEIN

If he sees it he never can destroy it!

MONG

We will all bring out our work!

(*They run into the houses.* ZAR *and* ZAN, *who have been huddled together, attentive, come out of the corner.*)

ZAN

(*Very anxious.*) What is your plan?

ZAR

It hasn't come yet.

ZAN

Do you remember, once, how an old, old woman pulled yards and yards of shining stuff out of a nutshell?

ZAR

It was like a ribbon of spider web with the dew on it in the moonlight.

ZAN

I wish we had it here. We could sell it and give the gold to the weavers.

ZAR

A wish isn't a plan.

ZAN

We must think!

(*They shut their eyes and twist their bodies and screw up their faces.*)

ZAR

(*His eyes tight closed.*) I can see shining stuffs, all green and coral and turquoise. And petals of roses blowing over it. And gold, like ripening rice fields in the sun. And purple, like far hills at sunset time. If I could only weave, I could make the most wonderful cloth in the world.

ZAN

That isn't a plan, either.

ZAR

No. The plan hasn't come yet.

(*They think harder than ever.*)

ZAN

(*With a great leap.*) I have thought something!

ZAR

What?

ZAN

It is easy to make foolish people do what you want them to do!

ZAR

That is true! You have only to call out what is most foolish in them, and you can make them do anything you wish!

ZAN

Is there anything foolish in Han?

ZAR

Han is too wicked to be foolish.

ZAN

(*Cautiously.*) Is there anything foolish in the emperor?

(*They think hard.*)

ZAR

(*With secrecy.*) I have thought of something foolish in the emperor.

ZAN

Tell it to me.

ZAR

He cares about nothing but clothes.

ZAN

We must think about that!

(*They almost have convulsions with the intensity of their thought. The* EMPEROR'S *music is heard, distant, approaching. The weavers enter in haste, and kneel, putting their bundles of weaving beside them, ready to kowtow to the* EMPEROR *as soon as he appears. The* EMPEROR *enters, preceded by the* GONG BOY *and* HAN. *After kowtowing three times, the weavers lift their stuffs, holding them out to the* EMPEROR, *beseechingly. The* EMPRESS *walks with the* EMPEROR. *She is entranced with the stuffs. She is very young and very pretty.*)

HAN

Put up your stuffs. They are not fit for the eyes of the emperor to rest on.

WEAVERS

(*Supplicating.*) Let us show you our work. See! Look at the beauty of it. Etc.

EMPEROR

Tell them to be silent.

HAN

Silence!

EMPEROR

Tell them my will.

HAN

Bow to the ground before your emperor. Hear his august word. (*They prostrate themselves.*) You have become a shame to your trade! You have left the patterns of your fathers for new and easy ones! You have used glass for jewels!

EMPRESS

(*Eagerly.*) Those jewels are not glass.

HAN

(*To the* EMPEROR.) You see? It is as I have told you. The empress is too stupid to know real jewels from false.

EMPEROR

(*Uneasy.*) The empress should not be stupid.

HAN

If it is the will of the emperor, I will instruct the empress for an hour every morning and an hour every evening. Then she may learn to tell pure jewels. She will no longer be stupid. The emperor will not need to send her away.

(*The* EMPRESS *gasps and shrinks, wide-eyed with terror at the thought, but murmurs under her breath.*)

EMPRESS

I do not want to be with Han. I do not like him.

EMPEROR

I should not like to send her away.

HAN

A stupid person is not fit to be empress.

EMPEROR

You shall instruct the empress.

(*Weavers who have looked up during this, reach their goods to the* EMPRESS, *murmuring.*)

WEAVERS.

Your eyes are true. You are right. The jewels are pure. Etc.

(HAN *gives a signal to the gong, which is sounded and they prostrate themselves again.*)

HAN

You have tried to deceive the empress, because she is stupid. For this your looms shall be broken and your weaving destroyed. You shall bear this unfit stuff before me to my rooms in the palace, that I may see it cut to pieces and utterly destroyed.

FAH

(*Above cries of grief and rage from the weavers.*) You will sell it! You will make yourself rich on it! (*To the* EMPEROR.) He is robbing us, because we refuse to give him half the price.

CROWD

(*Wildly.*) He's a cheat! He takes our money! The empress is right! He starves us! He's grinding us down! Etc.

(*Great pounding on the gong. The* EMPRESS *struggles between her desire to defend her judgment and her fear of* HAN, *but the fear is greater and keeps her silent. The* EMPEROR *lifts a hand, his eyes flashing. There is sudden and absolute silence.*)

EMPEROR

Han is my minister. His word is my word.

(ZAR *and* ZAN *think, desperately.*)

HAN

From this day you are no longer the royal weavers. I will find others to live in these houses and weave the patterns that have been used in this street from early times.

TSEIN

Great emperor, our fathers have taught us. There are in the whole land no others who know the secret ways to weave for the emperor.

HAN

If there are none in this land I will fetch them from other lands.

ZAR

(*Softly to* ZAN.) It has come! (*He crosses to the* EMPEROR, *and kowtows.* ZAN *follows, at his heels.*) Great emperor, we are weavers from a far-away land. We can weave you a stuff that is like no other stuff in the world. We can weave a power into it, that no one else under the sun or moon can weave into cloth.

EMPEROR

What power is that?

ZAR

Our stuff has this wonderful quality. It cannot be seen by any one who is stupid, or unfit for the position he holds.

(HAN *turns away, startled.* EMPRESS *frightened. Weavers, amazed, eager.*)

EMPEROR

That is capital stuff! If I had a robe of that,

I could tell what people about me are not fit to hold the positions they have!

ZAR

(*Cutting off* HAN *who is about to protest.*) That is true, great emperor! If you had a minister of your robes, who was dishonest, or not fit to be your minister, he would be afraid to have you order the stuff, even! He would say it could not be true. But Great Han has no fear.

ZAN

See how eager he is to have you order the stuff!

ZAR

You can tell by that, that Han is honest and fit for the position he holds.

HAN

Uh—yes, your majesty. You must order the stuff woven at once.

EMPEROR

What price do you ask for this wonderful stuff?

ZAR

We ask nothing at all. Our pay is our joy in what we do.

ZAN

We need only twenty chests of the purest gold, and twenty jars of the costliest jewels and we can begin at once.

ZAR

That is all we ask.

ZAN

Only bid Han give us a room in the palace where we may set up our loom, and the stuff shall be woven by this time to-morrow, and the garments cut and sewed by noon.

EMPEROR

I can hardly wait until to-morrow! In the afternoon I will walk through all the streets of the city, to show the people my wonderful new clothes! Fetch your loom at once! I will send gold and silk and jewels for your weaving from the royal stores! As for these bad weavers, Han shall deal with them as he will.

(*He moves out, to his music, leading the* EMPRESS. HAN *motions to the weavers, after the* EMPEROR'S *exit.*)

HAN

Lift up your bundles. Bear them before me to the palace. You shall leave them there. To-morrow, I will make way with them. When they are destroyed, you shall be driven out of the city.

(*The weavers lift their bundles and stumble out, bowed with grief. The* GONG BOY *crosses to* HAN, *strikes his gong, and they exit as they entered.* ZAR *and* ZAN *leap out, and hug each other with joy.*)

ZAN

We are going to the emperor's palace!

ZAR

He will send us silk and gold and jewels!

ZAN

We will give them to the weavers!

ZAR

It will be enough to make them rich for a year!

ZAN

We must find a strange loom.

ZAR

We must find out what people do when they weave!

ZAN

I will go among the people and find out how to weave!

ZAR

I will go and search out a strange loom!

BOTH

This will be the best adventure we ever had!

(*Exit, laughing and leaping.*)

CURTAIN

ACT II

A room in HAN'S *quarters, in the palace. A decorated panel with jewels on it, one great ruby especially brilliant. It should be as big as a pigeon's egg. Chest, bags of gold, and box of silk thread. Chest not too large to be handled easily by one, and hidden in the cupboard—about the size of a large shoe box, but carven and glittering with jewels and gold.*

ZAR *is alone, examining the loom. He does not understand at all, how cloth could be made on it, and is very anxious. A great gong, different from that of the* GONG BOY, *is struck, off, and* ZAR *jumps and runs about in fright. He gets himself together and stands by the loom.* ZAN *leaps in.* ZAR *runs to seize him.*

ZAR

Zan! I heard the gong! I thought Han was coming!

ZAN

The gong is the signal to open the gate! It always sounds, when any one is coming, no matter who it is. It has a very different sound from Han's gong.

ZAR

I am glad you are here.

ZAN

You act frightened.

ZAR

Han sent word he is coming to see the stuff! He will expect us to weave. Have you found out how?

ZAN

I found an old man to teach me. I practiced all night long.

ZAR

Show me! Quick!

ZAN

OH! This is a fine loom you found!

ZAR

I can think of fine stuff when I look at it. But I couldn't find out how to weave.

ZAN

(*Illustrating with his hands.*) There are a thousand threads, running from top to bottom, like strings on a lyre.

ZAR

(*Shutting his eyes and having a good time.*) I see them! Bright threads! They make a rainbow on the loom.

ZAN

In the shuttle are more threads.

ZAR

I can't see the shuttle. (*Opening his eyes.*) I don't know what it is.

ZAN

It is this shape. In it, there is a long spool. On it, is wound a long, long thread.

ZAR

(*Shutting his eyes.*) I see it! Gold thread! Shining! Fine as a spider weaves!

ZAN

(*Illustrating.*) You pass the shuttle under the threads on the loom, then under, then over, then under—if you keep on long enough, it's cloth!

ZAR

(*His eyes screwed up in his ecstasy.*) I see it! With patterns in it! Like the shadow of many leaves! And stars, in a pool!

ZAN

Come and practice.

ZAR

We'll pretend to put the bobbin through.

(*They sit, one on each side of the loom, on their heels, and go through the motions of throwing the shuttle back and forth.*)

ZAN

Under. Over. Under. Over. Under! Over! Faster! Faster! Faster yet!

(*They work so fast that they break down, laughing.* ZAR *stops suddenly, pointing to the chest and bags.*)

ZAR

Oh! We must hide the gold and jewels and silk the emperor sent us to weave our stuff of! If Han sees them he will know we haven't woven them up!

ZAN

We must put them out of sight, and pretend we have woven them into wonderful thread that no one can see.

ZAR

Where shall we put them? (*They run about, looking.*) There is no place in this room to hide anything.

ZAN

That is strange.

ZAR

I don't like this room. I feel as if sly things went on here. I think Han has secrets here.

ZAN

He couldn't have things to hide. There are no chests to hide them in.

ZAR

Han wouldn't have chests. He has dark ways of doing things.

ZAN

It is a very fine room. Look at that great jewel, in the panel, there.

ZAR

I don't like that ruby. It makes me creepy. I feel as if there were blood on it. And tears.

ZAN

It is as large as a pigeon's egg.

ZAR

I think it is larger.

ZAN

(*Feeling it.*) No, it isn't.

ZAR

(*Feeling it.*) It spreads my fingertips more than a pigeon's egg does. Oh!!! It has come off!

ZAN

Hide it. Quick! Before Han comes!

ZAR

Han would miss it. There is a hole where it was.

ZAN

I feel my head coming off this very minute! Put it back! Put it back!

ZAR

It won't go!

ZAN

Twist it! Press hard!

(ZAR *does. The panel parts silently, one side moving right, the other left. It re-*

veals shelves piled with treasure, chests of gold, jars of jewels, and much glittering stuff. Conspicuous is the piece TSEIN *held up, which the* EMPRESS *noticed.* ZAR *and* ZAN *are so startled that they leap backward, colliding and falling over each other. They get untangled and approach the outlay in awe.*)

ZAR

Look! There is the most beautiful thing of Tsein's life.

ZAN

And there is the stuff Fah was carrying.

ZAR

This is all the stuff he has stolen from the weavers! And bags of gold! And jars of jewels! Look! Look!

(*The great gong is struck.*)

ZAN

The great gates are opening!

ZAR

Han is coming!

ZAN

We must shut these doors!

ZAR

Wait! Wait! We must hide these jewels the emperor sent us! In here!

ZAN

Put them behind the others so Han can't see them if he opens his doors.

ZAR

You push that door.

ZAN

You push that.

(*They close the doors and leap to the loom, but as soon as they take their hands off, the doors open again, silently. They close them again, and again they open as soon as they are not held. This happens three times.*)

ZAR

We must think about this!

ZAN

(*Running around.*) I can't think with Han out there, on his way to come in!

ZAR

You must think! Stop running around!

(*They think, with terrific concentration.*)

ZAN

(*Leaping.*) I have thought something!

ZAR

What?

ZAN

It is the ruby! We must put it back!

ZAR

It was on a secret spring!

(*They rush to shut the doors and screw the ruby in but are too excited to be accurate. It drops.*)

ZAN

Let me!

ZAR

Let me!

ZAN

Let me!! It is in! It stays!

(*They fall back with sighs of relief, but the doors open as before.* ZAN *seizes the ruby and runs about with it.*)

ZAR

(*Clasping his head.*) I've thought something, without even trying!

ZAN

What?! What?!!

ZAR

We must put it in before we shut the doors!

(*They twist the ruby frantically, seizing it from each other, dropping it, running after it wilder and wilder.*)

ZAN

Hurry! Han is near!

ZAR

(*Stopping short.*) We are acting like sheep

when a wolf is near. We must act like men! Stand still! What is the first thing to do?

ZAN

You stand still, too.

ZAR

I am. What next?

ZAN

Hold the ruby firmly so it won't drop.

ZAR

What next?

ZAN

Look at the hole to see how it fits.

ZAR

I see. What next?

ZAN

Put it where it fits.

(ZAR *makes one direct movement and it stays.*)

ZAR

It is in!

ZAN

(*Running to help.*) Now shut the doors.

(*The doors stay closed. They take their hands from them cautiously, and start back several times, but they do not open again. They rush to the loom, ready to pretend to weave.*)

ZAR

When Han comes, I'll feel afraid.

ZAN

Han will not know there is nothing on the loom. He'll think it is because he has told lies to the emperor and robbed the weavers that he sees nothing on the loom.

ZAR

He'll pretend that he sees the stuff!

ZAN

We must pretend that he does, too!

ZAR

We must describe the stuff to him so that he will know what to say!

ZAN

You do that. You see things that aren't there so much better than I do.

ZAR

Oh, I'll make up fine things! Colors! And patterns!—— (*As some one is heard at the door.*) Weave!

ZAN

(*In swift whisper.*) Don't look up till he speaks. By that time he won't show how he feels when he can't see the stuff.

ZAR

This is exciting!

(*They weave rapidly, not looking up. The*

door is thrown open and the GENERAL *enters, marked by the flags worn on his back. He is smiling complacently, having no fear that he will not see the stuff. He is about to speak, when he sees the empty loom. He can hardly believe his eyes. It had never occurred to him to fear the test. He gulps, and looks away and back again. He is overwhelmed, and struggles for composure. The rogues weave away, apparently unconscious of his presence.* GENERAL *poses himself carefully before he speaks.)*

GENERAL

(*Swallowing hard.*) Uh—that is very wonderful stuff.

(*The two leap to their feet, whirling around to face the* GENERAL.)

ZAR

We thought great Han was coming.

GENERAL

I am a general in the emperor's army. Han sent me ahead. He wished me to report to him on the stuff.

ZAR

Look, then. Is it not lovely?

GENERAL

It is enchanting.

ZAN

I am sure you never saw anything like it before.

GENERAL

No. No, I never saw anything quite like it before.

ZAR

That is not strange. There *is* nothing like it in the whole world.

ZAN

Do you like the colors?

GENERAL

They are—uh—most unusual. (*Making a great bluff.*) I would not know how to name that color, right there.

ZAR

That is red.

GENERAL

Oh, yes, yes. Yes. Red. Of course. I—I meant —— What shade of red would you call it?

ZAR

That is coral.

GENERAL

Coral. Yes. Coral.

ZAR

I like best the green and turquoise and amethyst, all shining together.

GENERAL

Oh, the green—it is superb. And the—the ——

ZAR

Turquoise.

GENERAL

Yes, the turquoise. I must tell Han about—(*fixing them in his mind*) the green and the turquoise.

ZAR

And the amethyst.

GENERAL

Oh! Oh, yes. The amethyst.

ZAR

And see the gold, like the sun on ripening rice fields.

GENERAL

(*His courage growing.*) Oh, Han will like the gold. Yes, it is like the sun on a yellowing field of rice.

ZAN

What else do you like?

GENERAL

(*Wiping his brow.*) Uh—I like it all.

ZAR

I like this purple, with the look of far hills at twilight time.

GENERAL

Yes, that is one of the finest things of all. (*Memorizing.*) Green, and gold and purple and coral and turquoise——

ZAN

Touch it. It is so light and airy, you would think there was nothing there at all.

GENERAL

(*Swallowing.*) My fingers are too clumsy to touch such a fine-spun web. I—I will go at once and tell Han how beautiful it is.

(*He goes in almost indecent haste.* ZAR *and* ZAN *seize each other in spasms of laughter.*)

ZAN

It is a fine plan you thought of!

ZAR

The general is a strong man, yet he was afraid to tell the truth.

ZAN

He is foolish!

ZAR

Every one is a little foolish. Every one will be afraid to tell the truth!

ZAN

Han was afraid to come, even! He sent the general ahead to find out for him!

(*The great gong sounds, and then* HAN'S *gong sounds off, approaching.*)

ZAR

Weave!

(*They spring to the loom and make-believe to weave swiftly. The* GENERAL *reënters, followed by* HAN. *The* GONG BOY *stops at the door.* HAN *casts a swift desperate look at the loom as he enters, then makes elaborate pretense of not having looked.*)

GENERAL

(*Bowing low.*) Great Han, here is the wonderful stuff.

HAN

(*Carefully turning his back to the loom.*) I shall have to look for myself, before I can believe the extravagant things you say.

GENERAL

(*Purple with anger.*) What reason have you to doubt the things I say?

HAN

They sound like things one imagines. Purple, and gold, and coral ——

GENERAL

I am a general in the emperor's army. I command a hundred thousand men for every flag I wear on my back. Is that not proof that I speak the truth?

HAN

High position is not proof of a man's word.

ZAN

That is true, high Han.

GENERAL

(*Puffing.*) I have heard the only proof you will accept is gold in your hand!

HAN

The proof I will accept is what my own eyes tell me! If you have lied to me about the splendor of this stuff, I shall have you punished, in spite of your flags!

GENERAL

You are nothing but a buyer of cloth! You cannot punish a general in the emperor's army!

HAN

I am the minister of the emperor's robes! One new dress is more to the emperor than his whole army! I can punish any man I please! Stand aside. I will see the stuff these men have made. (*He turns elaborately to the loom, and makes an exaggerated gesture of surprise and delight.*) Ah-h-h-h! You did not say half enough! Ah, that green! That turquoise! And the gold! It reminds me of a rice field I saw once, at harvest time!

ZAR

With the low sun slanting over it.

HAN

Yes! It is like the sun on a harvest field of rice! The emperor must see this at once.

ZAN

We are ready to fit the garments on him.

HAN

(*Cautiously.*) Are all the garments made of the same cloth?

BOTH

(*With a bow.*) All the same.

HAN

They all have green and coral and purple and gold?

BOTH

All.

ZAN

But every one has a different pattern in the middle of the back.

HAN

Oh. A different pattern. Uh —— What is the pattern in the middle of the great train?

ZAR

That is like the shadow of many leaves. And below, stars in a pool. And the border is purple, like far-away hills at twilight time.

HAN

Hm-m. Shadow of many leaves. Stars in a pool. That sounds a little dull.

ZAN

With a jewel in each star.

HAN

Ah. A jewel in each star. That ought to please the emperor. Yes. And the border, like ripening rice fields, did you say?

GENERAL

(*Who has been moving his lips to form each word.*) Oh, no, no, no, no.—The border is like far-away hills at twilight time.

HAN

Yes. Yes, of course. Purple. I am glad of that. I should not have liked gold in the border. And what shall you make of the piece on the loom?

ZAR

That is for the undermost garment of all.

HAN

Oh. The undermost garment of all.

ZAR

The great train is woven and sewed, and the splendid outer garment, and the long tunic under that, and the short tunic under that, and the beautiful long trousers, and the glittering shoes. But the straight little shirt that goes next to the sacred body of the emperor, is not yet cut or sewed. It lacks one inch of the weaving.

ZAN

It will be done by the time you fetch the emperor.

HAN

Are not coral and turquoise and gold too beautiful for the undermost garment of all?

ZAR

Nothing is too beautiful to touch the sacred body of the emperor!

HAN

That is true. The emperor is waiting outside the gates, under the pomegranate trees. I will fetch him at once. (*On his way out he stops to examine the ruby in the panel. The rogues stiffen with terror and move together.*) The servants have left finger marks on my great ruby. I will have them lashed a thousand times!

(*Exit* HAN *and the* GENERAL.)

ZAN

I have thought a fine thing!

ZAR

What?

ZAN

Han will bring the emperor. If we let the emperor know that Han sees nothing on the loom, he will not trust Han any more!

ZAR

He will take his position away from him!

ZAN

Then he cannot beat and rob the weavers!

ZAR

The emperor must know!

ZAN

We must let the emperor catch Han in his lies!

ZAR

But Han must not catch the emperor!

ZAN

What is your plan?

ZAR

It hasn't come yet.

(*A knock, from a different side than the door is on.*)

ZAN

What was that?

ZAR

Somebody knocked.

ZAN

(*At the door.*) There is nobody here.

(*Another knock.*)

ZAR

It came from there.

ZAN

That couldn't be. There is no door.

(*As they stare at the place, a panel slides back, and an arm comes through, holding a great fan. They step back in awe. The arm belongs to the* EMPRESS, *who enters, holding her great fan in front of her face, her other hand groping before her.*)

EMPRESS

(*To herself, frightened.*) I wonder which way the loom is.

ZAN

It is here.

EMPRESS

Oh-h-h—who is that?

ZAN

We are the weavers from a far-away land.

EMPRESS

(*In great agitation.*) Why did you not answer when I knocked?

ZAR

We could not find the door.

EMPRESS

(*More and more terrified.*) There is no door. It is a secret passage of the emperor. You should have called out. Then I would have gone away.

(*She sways and slips down in a faint. They run to her.*)

ZAR

(*In terror.*) She has gone to her ancestors!

ZAN

She has a crown on her head!

ZAR

It is the empress! (ZAN *kowtows, madly.*) Get up! Get up! She can't see what you are doing.

ZAN

What if Han finds her here!

ZAR

(*Peering gently under the fan.*) How beautiful she is.

ZAN

How still.

ZAR

I feel a soft breath on my hand!

ZAN

She is not with her ancestors!

ZAR

Her spirit is only a little way off!

ZAN

(*Fanning furiously with the first thing to come to hand.*) Bring it back!

ZAR

(*Also fanning wildly.*) Quick! Before Han comes with the emperor!

ZAN

Fan hard!

(*The* EMPRESS *sits up, slowly. They stop fanning to watch her.*)

EMPRESS

You are blowing my hair about.

ZAR

We are blowing your spirit back to your body.

EMPRESS

It is back.

ZAN

Why did it go away?

EMPRESS

I was afraid. Oh-h-h! I am afraid again!

(*She faints again and they call to her frantically.*)

BOTH

No, no, no! Do not be afraid.—Do not be afraid!

ZAR

We must be more gentle.

BOTH

(*Very gentle.*) Do not be afraid.

(*She sits up again, her fan still held in front of her face.*)

ZAN

Why are you afraid?

EMPRESS

I was afraid you would tell the emperor that I came here. Oh-h-h-h ——

(*She swoons more deeply.*)

ZAN

(*Into her ear.*) Come back. We will not tell.

ZAR

She is too far away. She cannot hear.

ZAN

(*Louder.*) We will not tell!

ZAR

She is still too far away.

(*They lift her between them, one at each ear.*)

BOTH

(*Shouting.*) We will not tell!!!

EMPRESS

(*Looking about dazedly.*) Did you say something?

ZAN

We said that we would not tell the emperor that you came here.

EMPRESS

(*Getting to her feet in haste.*) If you should tell the emperor, he would believe what Han says.

ZAR

We heard what Han said.

ZAN

He says you are stupid.

ZAR

He says you are not fit to be empress.

EMPRESS

Yes. So the emperor wants to know whether I see the stuff. He wants to watch me look at it, the first time. He ordered me to stay in my inner room, and speak to no one who had seen the stuff. He is going to send for me to come and see it when he is here. I cannot bear to be watched when I look. That is why I came in secret.

ZAN

Look, then.

EMPRESS

I am afraid to look.

ZAR

Do not be afraid.

EMPRESS

If I cannot see the stuff, the emperor will send me away. I cried real tears, from the evening star to the morning star, for fear I could not see it.

ZAR

You cannot be unfit to be empress. You are beautiful. (*This comforts the* EMPRESS.) You are wise. (*This fills her with doubt.*) You are good. (*This makes her widen her eyes and pucker her face.*)

EMPRESS

(*Courageously.*) I will look! (*She makes a little run to the loom, and lowers her fan a little, but jerks it up again in a panic before she can see the loom.*) Turn your backs. You must not watch me look. I could not bear it to be watched.

(*They turn their backs, but twist their heads around to watch her. They are so alert that though she turns suddenly once or twice, she does not catch them. She makes several attempts to screw up her courage sufficiently to face the test, but can never quite bring herself to do it.*)

ZAN

Have you looked?

EMPRESS

I can't get my fan down enough.

ZAN

I will put your fan down for you.

EMPRESS

(*Waving him back desperately.*) Oh, no, no, no, no. Look the other way. (*At last she gets her fan below her eyes, and peers over it at the empty loom. She lowers it slowly, staring, aghast. Her face quivers and she bursts into tears.* ZAR *and* ZAN *are aghast that she is about to acknowledge she sees nothing. They seize each other, and think wildly.*) I can't—— (*Sobs.*) I can't—— (*Sobs.*) I can't—— (*More sobs.*)

ZAR

(*Running to her.*) You cannot keep the sacred water drops from your eyes. Zan! The beauty of our stuff moves the empress to tears!

(*The* EMPRESS *lifts her head and checks her sobs.*)

ZAN

The empress' tears are the highest praise our stuff could have.

ZAR

(*Clearly, with intention.*) The green, and the turquoise, and the gold like the sun slanting over a ripening field of rice, and the purple like far hills at twilight time, make even the empress weep with joy.

(*The* EMPRESS *turns her head to them and follows the above closely, a little ghost of a nod marking her fixing of each word.*)

ZAN

Ah, yes. When I look long at it, I weep too.

ZAR

And the pattern, like the shadow of many leaves, is like sad memories of beautiful things that are gone.

ZAN

It is not strange that her eyes brim over.

ZAR

She would not be fit to be empress if our stuff did not hurt her heart with its beauty.

EMPRESS

(*To herself.*) It would be terrible not to be empress.

ZAR

I am glad the empress came to look in secret. She might have wept before all the people to-morrow, when she saw the emperor in his wonderful new clothes.

ZAN

The people might not understand.

ZAR

Han would never understand.

ZAN

Even the emperor might not understand that the empress wept because the beauty of our stuff moved her to tears.

ZAR

When she talks to the emperor about the wonderful colors, he will see that she is not stupid.

EMPRESS

(*Softly, to herself.*) The green, and the turquoise, and the gold, and the purple——

ZAN

Like far-away hills at twilight time.

ZAR

And the pattern, like the shadow of many leaves.

EMPRESS

Like sweet memories.—Like sad memories—of beautiful things that are gone.

(*The gong sounds, and the* EMPEROR'S *music, approaching, immediately after.*)

ROGUES

The emperor!

EMPRESS

He will send for me! (*She runs to the panel through which she entered.* ZAN *shuts it after her. As the two leap to the loom, she sticks her head in again.*) You will not tell the emperor?

ZAN

(*Urging her out again.*) No, no!

EMPRESS

(*Sticking her head in.*) When I come in you must act as if you had never seen me.

ZAN

Yes, yes, yes!

EMPRESS

(*Head in again.*) Don't let him send for me right away. I must wash the tears from my face.

ZAN

(*Desperately hurrying her.*) He is almost here!

EMPRESS

I will go.

(ZAN *shuts the panel after her, and leaps back to the loom. The* EMPEROR'S *music is very near by now.*)

ZAR

We must pretend the stuff is done.

ZAN

We have taken it from the loom.

ZAR

The finished garments are folded, and piled over there.

EMPRESS

(*Head in, breathless with haste.*) Give me plenty of time to wash the tears from my face.

ZAN

The sooner you go the more time you will have.

EMPRESS

(*Head in just as* ZAN *gets in position by the loom.*) I have gone.

(*Exit.*)

ZAR

We must pretend to be making the undermost garment of all.

ZAN

I will be cutting it.

ZAR

I will be threading the needle. So.

ZAN

What shape is the undermost garment of all?

ZAR

(*Drawing a picture in the air.*) Like this.

ZAN

How are you going to let the emperor catch Han in his lies?

ZAR

The plan hasn't come yet.

(*They cut and sew intently as the* EMPEROR *enters, ushered in by* HAN.)

EMPEROR

(*Turning back to* GENERAL *at the door.*) Fetch the empress at once.

ROGUES

(*Whirling to kowtow.*) The emperor!

(*The* EMPEROR *blinks at the loom, shuts his eyes, blinks again. He draws a sharp breath of terror which he converts into a cough. He looks suddenly at* HAN, *and catches him leering as he watches him intently.*)

EMPEROR

(*In a fury.*) Why do you grin?

HAN

I am not grinning.

EMPEROR

You watched my face as a yellow cat watches a hole where a mouse may come out! What thought was stealing around in your mind when your eyes went sliding up and down my face?

HAN

I—uh—wished to rejoice my eyes in your delight when you saw the stuff.

EMPEROR

It is death to ferret for thoughts in your emperor's face. To your knees! (HAN *kowtows, like the rogues who are still prone. The* EMPEROR *steals in swift strides to the loom, gathering up his skirts to step over* ZAN, *who is in his path. The others lift their heads, like turtles, to watch as the* EMPEROR *stares at the loom, bends to touch the empty air. Feeling nothing he shrinks back in terror. He clutches his crown. Finally he returns to his original position, and takes up an imperial pose.*) Rise.

ZAR

Alas! The emperor is angry. We should have left the cloth on the loom till he came.

ZAN

We ask pardon that we took the stuff from the loom, to make it up into garments.

(EMPEROR'S *face is by now wreathed in smiles, as he realizes the cloth was not on the loom.*)

EMPEROR

Ah! Where have you put the garments?

ZAN

If the emperor will look behind him, he will see the garments folded and piled high.

ZAR

(*Pretending to hold up the shirt.*) All except this undermost garment of all, which I have cut and am about to sew.

(*Both* HAN *and the* EMPEROR *look dazedly at the empty chair.*)

HAN

(*Clearing his throat.*) Will the emperor be pleased to look at the great train these men have woven for you? Coral, and green, and purple, and gold, with a pattern like the shadow of many leaves in the middle of the back?

EMPEROR

They may show me their work.

ZAN

If great Han will turn the other way, I can fasten the train onto his shoulders that the emperor may see the colors shine as it sweeps the floor.

(HAN *turns, and* ZAN *makes-believe to shake out a train.*)

ZAR

I will help you spread it out.

ZAN

(*Whispering.*) Go and make up a plan.

ZAR

(*Also whispering.*) The plan won't come!

ZAN

(*Waving him away.*) Think!

(ZAR *returns to his pretense of sewing, but soon sits motionless, with his head clasped in his hands, his body screwed up.*)

HAN

(*Jumping as* ZAN *pretends to pin the train to*

his shoulder.) Ouch! You have put your pin through my coat!

ZAN

Forgive the pin, great Han. Walk, that the emperor may see the shimmer as you move. (HAN *walks, looking uneasily over his shoulder.* ZAN *makes-believe to carry the train and lay it in a sweeping curve.*) Do not the folds make you think of a rainbow?

EMPEROR

Those are colors such as I have never seen before.

ZAN

They are very rare colors. (*Lifting one after another imaginary garment.*) See the petals of roses blown across this splendid outer garment! And the border the color of a turquoise, at the bottom of this long tunic. If the emperor will remove his outer coat, I will slip this tunic over his head to make sure that it fits as it should.

EMPEROR

(*Dazedly.*) You may remove my coat.

(ZAN *removes the outer coat and throws it over the loom. He almost forgets* HAN'S *imaginary train, and but for a swift signal from* ZAR *would have stepped where it is supposed to be.*)

ZAN

(*Going through the motions of pulling a tunic over the* EMPEROR'S *head.*) If the emperor will lower his head. . . . Wait! Wait! It is caught. (*The* EMPEROR *ducks and twists, as* ZAN *indicates, trying hard to seem to know what it is all about.* ZAN, *stepping back.*) Marvelous! The tunic has the lines of a red lily, on the edge of a stream! The emperor has the look of a god! He is a pattern of beauty in this tunic. What will he be when all the new clothes are on!

(EMPEROR *bridles and preens himself, almost forgetting his plight in his satisfaction in the praise. The gong is struck without.*)

EMPEROR

The empress! Let no one speak till she has seen the stuff. Han, stand there, where the great train is plain from the door. I will stand here, where the tunic will greet her eyes as she enters.

(*Enter the* GENERAL, *followed by the* EMPRESS. *She looks around nervously, her breath coming faster with every pair of eyes she finds fastened on her in the silence.*)

EMPRESS

Look the other way. I cannot bear your eyes.

HAN

(*Maliciously.*) Why does the empress fear our eyes? (*She looks toward the loom, and seeing the* EMPEROR'S *coat on it, breaks into a triumphant little laugh.* HAN, *spitefully.*) Why does the empress laugh when she sees the emperor's *old* coat?

(*She stops short in her laugh, trembling.*

ZAN *makes-believe to spread the train more widely. Her face is working piteously.*)

ZAN

If great Han will turn a little more, the empress can better see the pattern, in the middle of the back of the stuff which I have pinned to his shoulders.

(HAN *turns, still watching the* EMPRESS *over his shoulder. The* EMPRESS *stares at the supposed train, and bursts into tears.*)

HAN

(*Triumphant.*) Why does the empress weep?

ZAN

(*Quickly and pointedly.*) It is the pattern, in the middle of the back. The beauty of it moves her to tears!

EMPRESS

(*Choking back her sobs.*) The pattern—like the shadow of many leaves, is like sweet memories—sad memories—of beautiful things that are gone.

EMPEROR

(*Delighted.*) Ah-h-h!

HAN

But why did she laugh when she first came in?

ZAN

The colors of the tunic I put on the emperor

when I removed the old coat make her laugh with joy.

EMPRESS

(*Looking at the* EMPEROR, *and tumbling the words out.*) The green, and the coral, and the turquoise, and the gold. It is like sunlight, dancing on a ripening field of rice.

ZAR

It makes her spirit dance too.

ZAN

She would not be fit to be empress if she was too stupid to feel the beauty of our stuff!

EMPEROR

(*Joyfully.*) Ah-h-h!! Han! You are wrong! The empress is not stupid!

(*She laughs and flutters over to the* EMPEROR, *smiling up at him. There is a commotion at the door as* FAH *breaks past the* GENERAL.)

FAH

(*Flinging himself at* HAN'S *feet.*) Great Han!

HAN

This is the most insolent of the weavers! Take him away!

FAH

I am not insolent now, great Han. See! I kneel! I knock my head against the floor! All the weavers pray by my voice! Hear me!

HAN

Why are you not outside the gates by now?

FAH

Do not drive us from the city! We cannot leave the shrines of our ancestors! Our fathers worshipped there before us, and their fathers before them! Our hearts will wither and die where they are not.

HAN

In an hour the emperor will pass through the streets in his new clothes. When he comes to yours, let the houses be empty and the doors shut!

FAH

We will serve you! We will give you gold! Only let us stay where our fathers have been!

HAN

If any of you is still in your street when the emperor comes, he shall die!

FAH

(*Turning to kowtow to the* EMPEROR, *and in so doing resting his foot on the* EMPEROR'S *coat on the loom.*) Emperor!

HAN

(*Seizing him and flinging him to the* GENERAL.) You have set foot on the emperor's coat! Take this man and have him lashed till his coat is in tatters and his knees will bear him up no more! Then thrust him into the street! Make haste to your fellows, weaver! If any are not gone when the emperor comes, they shall feel my wrath before they die!

(*The* GENERAL *leads* FAH *off.* ZAN *pounds on* ZAR'S *head in desperation.*)

ZAN

(*Whispering but intense.*) What is your plan?

ZAR

(*Rising, softly.*) It has come! (*He points to* HAN'S *feet, and gives a terrible cry.*) The train! The emperor's train! Your feet are on it! It will tear!

ZAN

Get off! Get off! Get off!

(HAN *steps aside, bewildered, in haste. The rogues redouble their cries.* HAN *jumps and stumbles around.*)

ZAR and ZAN

No, no! Not there! No! Get off the train!! Not there! Oh, no! no! No, no, no!!! Get off! Get off! Off! Off! Off!!!

(HAN *finally leaps clear across the stage in one terrified bound. The rogues cry out more wildly than before.*)

ZAR

(*Screaming.*) Your foot is on the undermost garment of all!

ZAN

(*Kneeling to lift it.*) Take your foot off!

BOTH

(*Kneeling one on either side and lifting first one foot and then the other.*) Lift your foot! Not that one! No!! The other! The other! The other! Oh-h-h! You have torn it to rags!

ZAR

(*Pretending to hold it up.*) Look, your majesty! He has ruined the undermost garment of all!

ZAN

When the emperor walks the streets this afternoon, he will have to wear one *not* of our weaving!

EMPEROR

I will have your head struck off for this!

HAN

(*On his knees.*) No, no! Mercy! Mercy! I did not mean to do it!

EMPEROR

(*To the* GENERAL.) Cast him into a dungeon till I decide how he shall be punished.

HAN

No! No! It was not my fault!

ZAR

Any one might step on it once!

ZAN

But why did you dance and stamp on it?

EMPEROR

It is death to stamp on the Emperor's robes!

HAN

I did not mean to stamp on it! I could not see the stu —— (*He catches himself, clapping his hand over his mouth.*)

(*The* EMPRESS *breaks the silence by laughing softly.* ZAR *and* ZAN *rejoice secretly. The* EMPEROR *stares in amazement, the significance of* HAN'S *slip dawning on him slowly.*)

EMPEROR

How?—Han is not fit to be my minister?—This is truly wonderful stuff, to find out a man's thoughts. (*To* ZAR *and* ZAN.) You have done me a great service. Ask what reward you will.

ZAR

As a keepsake of this room, the ruby, in the panel there, would be dear to us.

HAN

The great ruby! In my panel?

EMPEROR

Why do you stare? It is easily replaced.

HAN

The stone is dear to me. Give them some other.

EMPEROR

They shall have what they ask. They could have asked much more.

HAN

(*To* ZAR.) I will give you a topaz twice the size of that.

ZAR

The topaz would be too large, great Han.

ZAN

The ruby is just large enough.

HAN

I will give you thrice its worth in gold.

ZAN

That would be a great sum.

HAN

I will give you its worth ten times over, if you will take another stone and go your way.

EMPEROR

You set a great price upon it.

EMPRESS

(*Examining it.*) It is a very pure jewel.

ZAR

If the empress would give us the jewel with her own sacred hands, it would be worth all the other jewels in the world.

EMPRESS

(*Flattered.*) I do not know how to get it off.

ZAN

If the empress twists a little, perhaps ——

ZAR

And presses as she twists.

EMPRESS

So?

ZAR

Push on it.

EMPRESS

So?

ZAN

A little more——

(*The doors open. Every one cries out except* HAN, *the rogues most of all.*)

EMPEROR

How?!

HAN

(*Quick-witted.*) It is the bad work I took from the weavers. There has not been time to cut it to pieces!

EMPEROR

Is that all that there is in the hiding place?

HAN

That is all.

EMPEROR

There is nothing there but bad weaving and false jewels?

HAN

There is nothing else.

EMPEROR

(*To* GENERAL.) Bind him, and lock him safe. I myself will set out all this treasure to prove his words.

(*Exit* GENERAL *and* HAN. EMPEROR *turns to the treasure.*)

ZAR

Uh—uh—have a care! The tunic! It is thin as air! It is fragile as a butterfly's wing. Something may catch it.

EMPEROR

(*Looking in surprise at his stiff embroidered tunic.*) Fragile? (*Then he remembers.*) Oh! Oh, yes. Remove the tunic.

ZAN

Oh! The great train! Han has worn it away!

EMPEROR

Remove the train!

(ZAN *dashes off, and returns, as if carrying a folded garment.* ZAR *makes-believe to take the tunic from the* EMPEROR.)

ZAR

The hour for the procession through the streets is almost here. If the new clothes should feel strange to the Emperor he would not walk with the grace which makes the people praise him.

ZAN

They may feel strange. They are as light as a moonbeam that falls across the arm.

ZAR

They have no more weight than a dream.

ZAN

Would it not be well for the Emperor to walk about in them before he goes among the people?

ZAR

Then he would not feel strange in them when he walks through the streets.

EMPEROR

You have made a good plan. First, I will bathe in the pool under the pomegranate trees.

ZAN

If it is the will of the emperor, we will set out this stuff, while he is made ready for his wonderful new clothes.

ZAR

Then his eyes can judge of great Han's guilt.

ZAN

And his sacred hands will not be soiled.

EMPEROR

You may set out the stuffs.

ZAR

Is it the emperor's wish that we help him put on the garments we have made?

ZAR

They are sheer as the wings of a dragonfly,

and soft as the silk of a milkweed pod. They must be handled by one who knows.

EMPEROR

You shall array me with your own hands. When I am dressed, you shall carry the great train before the people. You shall wear rich garments, and chains of gold about your necks, and be called the imperial court weavers. (*To the* EMPRESS.) At last, I know you are not stupid. You shall return with me to judge this stuff. (*He leads her out, to his music.*)

ZAR

Quick! We must get the stuff the emperor sent us out of here!

ZAN

We will take it to the weavers!

ZAR

We will tell them Han has fallen, and they need not leave the city!

ZAN

We must run fast! Fah will hurry them away!

ZAR

(*Stops short, as they start to run, their arms full of the gold, etc.*) Oh!

ZAN

What?

ZAR

Do you know the way to the street?

ZAN

NO! Do you?

ZAR

No!

ZAN

We must ask the first man we meet. (*They start to run again.* ZAN *stops short.*) OH-h!

ZAR

What?

ZAN

Do you know the name of the street?

ZAR

No. Do you?

ZAN

No.

ZAR

Then how can we ask the first man we meet the way?

ZAN

We must run through all the streets till we find it.

ZAR

There are many streets!

ZAN

Then we must run fast!

ZAR

Yes! Or the weavers will be gone!

ZAN

And the emperor will send for us to put on his clothes!

ZAR

And if we are not there, off with our heads!

BOTH

Oh-h! (*Exit, running very fast.*)

CURTAIN

ACT III

The street of the royal weavers. The weavers sit in doorways and on steps, silent, bowed with anxiety. TSEIN *is in front with her child beside her. The* OLD WOMAN *is watching the entrance of the street, her eyes shaded by her hand, for better seeing.*

CHILD

Mother, I am hungry.

TSEIN

You must be patient, child of a weaver.

CHILD

I want a bowl of rice.

TSEIN

There is no more rice.

CHILD

But mother, I am hungry.

TSEIN

I have nothing to give you, little jade-drop.

CHILD

Let us go in and pray to our ancestor-gods for food.

TSEIN

I have prayed long.

CHILD

Do not the gods hear, mother?

TSEIN

Sh-h-h ——

OLD WOMAN

Fah is coming.

(*The people rise, tense, waiting.*)

CHILD

Where has Fah been, mother?

TSEIN

He has been to Han.

CHILD

Why did Fah go to Han, mother?

TSEIN

To beg him to let us stay in the homes of our fathers.

CHILD

Fah doesn't beg for what he wants. He speaks loud.

TSEIN

(*Deeply.*) Fah has begged Han for mercy.

OLD WOMAN

Fah walks wearily.

(*A wave of uneasiness sweeps over the group.*)

CHILD

Why does Fah walk wearily, mother?

TSEIN

His news is heavy in his feet.

OLD WOMAN

Fah's coat is in tatters.

(*Weavers show anger and despair.*)

CHILD

Why is Fah's coat in tatters, mother?—Mother! Do you know why Fah's coat is in tatters?

TSEIN

They have used the lash on him.

OLD WOMAN

Fah is here.

(*They all turn, silently, toward the end of the street.* FAH *enters, weak, in tatters. He shows his tatters. There is dead silence and stillness. He wavers and is about to fall. Some of them catch him and support him.*)

FAH

Give me to drink.

(*Some one swiftly puts a cup to his lips. He gathers strength and speaks.*)

CHILD

(*Before he speaks, in the deep silence.*) Why are you so still, mother?

TSEIN

Sh-h-h-h.

FAH

We are to leave the gods of our ancestors in the shrines our fathers have built and go forth.

OLD WOMAN

What is to happen will happen.

FAH

The emperor walks through the streets this afternoon, to show the people his wonderful new clothes. At every street he will stop, to let the people look their fill. When he comes here, the doors must be shut and the houses empty. If any is still here, he will die.

OLD WOMAN

Let us go in. Be swift to gather up what you will carry from the city.

FAH

Be very swift. My knees would not bear me up and I was long in coming. By now, the emperor will be upon his way.

(*They go into the houses.* ZAR *and* ZAN *enter, running.* ZAR *stops so suddenly that they collide.*)

ZAN

Why did you stop?

ZAR

I felt as if this were the street.

ZAN

Why did you feel like that?

ZAR

I don't know.

ZAN

You must know.

ZAR

I think it is the street. I haven't any reason.

ZAN

You can't think a thing is true without a reason.

ZAR

It is often done.

ZAN

That is true. But then, people make up reasons.

ZAR

I don't like made up reasons.

ZAN

It must be the way it makes you feel.

ZAR

That is it!

ZAN

How does it make you feel?

ZAR

I don't know. I feel things, but I don't know what they are.

ZAN

You can't feel things without knowing what they are!

ZAR

I do it all the time!

ZAN

I remember something!

ZAR

What?

ZAN

There was a sign!

ZAR

It said, the street of—of ——

ZAN

The street of—of ——

ZAR

It won't come!

ZAN

I know how to make it come.

ZAR

How?

ZAN

Stop trying. Then it will pop into your head all of a sudden.

ZAR

What if it pops too late?

ZAN

It is almost too late, now.

ZAR

I feel as if the weavers were getting ready to leave this minute!

ZAN

Something has popped into my head!

ZAR

What?

ZAN

If this is the street, the sign will be *here*.

ZAR

Maybe we will remember what it is if we see it!

ZAN

Look for a sign! (*They look everywhere except in the right place. Finally they stand under the sign, discouraged.*) There is no sign.

ZAR

We have looked everywhere.

ZAN

This is not the street.

ZAR

We must run to the next street.

ZAN

There is not time. The emperor will be calling for us.

ZAR

If we go back now, the weavers will go out of the city! They will weep about it. They will never be happy again.

ZAN

(*With a sign of beheading.*) If we don't go back now, we'll wake up to-morrow without any heads!

ZAR

We must run!

(*They start, but* ZAN *stops short.*)

ZAN

We can't take these chests and bags of gold back to the palace!

ZAR

Let us hide them here!

ZAN

(*Pointing to a balcony, at the top of some steps.*) There is a good place.

ZAR

We can come back and get them after the emperor has showed the people his new clothes.

ZAN

We will be late! Run! Run!

(*They run off. One of the weavers peers out of the door.* LING *follows.*)

LING.

I thought I heard some one.

MONG

(*Following.*) There is no one here.

TSEIN

Is it safe to come out?

FAH

(*As the rest peer out, and enter cautiously.*) We must set off at once.

(*They gather, sobbing, their bundles on backs and shoulders.*)

OLD WOMAN

Kneel. We must take leave of our ancestors.

ALL

(*Chanting,* as they kneel.*) We must take leave of our ancestors.

FAH

(*Chanting.*) Shrines where our fathers have knelt——

ANOTHER

And their fathers before them——

OTHERS

And their fathers before *them*——

MORE

And their fathers before *them*——

FAH

(*Or any with a good voice.*) And their fathers' fathers till the stars were young——

* Music for this chant is available, or it can be intoned by the cast.

ONE

Farewell ——

OTHERS

Forever ——

ALL

Forever, farewell—farewell. Forever. Forever. Forever.

(*The chant trails away into a long held chord dying imperceptibly into silence. Faint and far, the* EMPEROR'S *music is heard against it. The weavers look up as it grows a little.*)

MONG

(*In a terrified whisper.*) The emperor's music!—Come ——

FAH

It is too late. We shall all die.

(*They all get to their feet.*)

OLD WOMAN

Go inside. Shut the doors.

LING.

Han may think that we are gone.

FAH

Let no one look out!

OLD WOMAN

Let no one answer, if any calls!

(*They go swiftly and silently off. The music grows.* CITIZENS *enter, aflutter with excitement from many directions.*)

FIRST CITIZEN

(*Meeting others.*) Have you seen the wonderful new clothes?

OTHERS

(*Cautious.*) No. No.

ANOTHER

My neighbor says that his wife says that her friend says that they are brighter than a rainbow!

ANOTHER

And shot with colors, and gold like the sun on a ripening field of rice!

ANOTHER

They say they are set with jewels, like stars in a pool!

FIRST

Every one is talking about it!

OTHERS

We mustn't miss it!

SECOND

People are quite carried away with the beauty of them!

ANOTHER

They say the emperor walks like a God!

SEVERAL

(*As the music increases.*) He is coming!

(*They run to look off, and kneel to kowtow,*

as the EMPEROR *enters, walking with majestic grace, bowing and posing, clad only in his crown and a scrap of an undershirt. The* CITIZENS *rise, at his word, shoot frightened glances from him to each other, and burst into a chorus of Ohs and Ahs, intermingled with " green," " coral," etc., a little belated, and much overdone.)*

EMPEROR

Rise.

(*As the chorus increases the* EMPEROR, *smiling fatuously at their enthusiasm, switches and poses, believing he is showing off his clothes. He smiles graciously at the* EMPRESS *and the* GENERAL *who preceded him, bowing and walking backward, and at* ZAN *and* ZAR *who, gorgeously dressed, make-believe to carry the train.)*

ZAR

If the emperor will walk in a circle, the people can see how the folds shimmer, as they fall in a crescent, like the little new moon.

EMPEROR

I will walk. (*He moves to music around the stage, pausing to pose and indulging in the airs and graces which he believes show off his garments. The people applaud more and more wildly at every pause, as he looks at them expectantly.* [*If the* EMPEROR *has the ability, the lines can be changed to suggest that the* EMPEROR *dances before the people. In that case, the rogues should move the people back to clear more room for the dance. Chinese dancing is highly stylized posturing and walking and is delightful when used here.*])

ZAN

(*At an opportune pause, in a whisper to* ZAR.) Something has popped into my head!

ZAR

What?

ZAN

The Street of the Royal Weavers!

ZAR

(*At another pause.*) Something has popped into mine!

ZAN

What?

ZAR

It was over a gate!

(*They both look at the gate and see the sign. As they come to the doors of the houses, as the* EMPEROR *walks, and ends his display, they listen at a door.*)

ZAN

Some one is crying.

ZAR

A plan has come! (*He leaps to the* EMPEROR *and kowtows.* ZAN *follows.*) Great and most beautiful emperor, this is the street of your royal weavers. No one in all the city is so worthy to see the emperor's glory as they.

GENERAL

They have left the city.

ZAN

I hear weeping within.

GENERAL

Han ordered them to be gone when the emperor came.

ZAR

Will the emperor order the doors to be open and his faithful weavers called out?

EMPEROR

Beat on the doors. Call to any who are there to come out.

GENERAL

(*Beating on the doors.*) Come out!

ZAN and ZAR

(*At the doors.*) The emperor calls you to come out!

(*The weavers enter, frightened, despairing, expecting death. They are slow to see the* EMPEROR'S *nakedness. When they do, they look at each other, humbled. Some cover their faces; some kneel. One or two murmur.*)

WEAVERS

We are not fit.

EMPEROR

How is this?

(*The weavers remember to kowtow at his voice.*)

ZAR

Great emperor, they are true children of the loom. Their hearts melt at the wonder of your new clothes.

ZAN

They do not feel themselves fit to gaze on your splendor.

EMPEROR

(*Pleased.*) They have a nice feeling. (*To the* GENERAL.) Fetch Han, from the guard. (*Exit* GENERAL.) Tell them to rise.

ZAR and ZAN

The emperor bids you rise.

(*The weavers rise, and stand dumb, eyes downcast, awaiting doom. The* GENERAL *enters, with* HAN. HAN'S *hands are bound. There is a murmur of surprise from the citizens, then from the weavers who look up at the sound.*)

EMPEROR

Han! Look upon my new clothes! Tell the people what you see!

HAN

(*Abject, bully that he is.*) I see nothing at all.

It is to me as if the emperor wore only his undermost garment of all.

(*An excited buzz from the crowd, hatred and triumph. Some self-conscious at being in the same boat with* HAN. *Many too rejoiced at his disgrace to remember their own plight.*)

EMPEROR

Tell the people what you have done, that you are unfit to be my minister, and blind to my wonderful stuff.

HAN

I have robbed and beaten and starved the weavers. I have made myself rich on the emperor's robes.

EMPEROR

For long I have trusted this man! I put the fate of my faithful weavers in his hands. Now I trust them! The empress, whom Han tried to make me believe a stupid person for his own ends, has seen the stuff they wove. She says the jewels are pure and the patterns the royal patterns from the days of their fathers. I now put the fate of Han in their hands. (*To weavers.*) Judge this man. How shall he be punished?

FAH

Put him to death!

(*A great supporting outcry from the weavers.* HAN *sinks to his knees, his hands in supplication.*)

OLD WOMAN

Death is soon over. Drive him from the city.

WEAVERS

Send him away!

EMPEROR

(*To* GENERAL.) Thrust him out of the city gates!

GENERAL

To your feet!

(HAN *stumbles out with the* GENERAL, *the weavers menacing and muttering as he goes.*)

EMPEROR

Take up the train. There are many streets where the wonderful stuff has not been seen.

ZAR

(*Kowtowing.*) I have thought a great thought.

EMPEROR

Tell your thought.

ZAR

If we stayed here, with your weavers, we could teach them our secrets while the sight of your robes is fresh in their eyes.

EMPEROR

That is a good thought.

ZAR

(*To bystanders.*) A great honor has come to

you. And you. You shall carry the emperor's train.

BYSTANDER

(*Terrified.*) I never carried an emperor's train in my life.

ZAN

We will show you.

ZAR

(*The two illustrating.*) You lift the train, so, together, and spread it, so, that the pattern of many leaves may be plain to see. And swing it together a little, so, as you walk, that the green and coral and purple may shine in the sun.

ZAN

Stand here.

ZAR

(*To the other.*) You, here.

ZAN

Hold out your hand.

ZAR

The cloth is very fragile. You must handle it like thistle-down.

(*They pretend to put the corners of the train into the bystanders' hands. Their victims watch them and each other out of the corner of their eyes, uncertain, then cautiously close their fingers.*)

ZAN

Not too tight! You will crush the folds!
(*Bystanders jump and fix their fingers.*)

ZAR

They are ready, your majesty.

ZAN

If the emperor will walk a few paces, that these lucky ones may follow the grace of his moving.

EMPEROR

(*Flattered.*) I will walk a few paces. (*He moves airily across and around.*)

(ZAR *and* ZAN *move with the bystanders, moving their arms in the right rhythm, and showing them how to imitate the* EMPEROR'S *walk as they pretend to swing the train. Gradually the bystanders, paralyzed with embarrassment at first, gain courage.*)

ZAR

Ah-h! That is right! Now it shines and shimmers! See the colors!

(*The* EMPEROR *looks around at the citizens and there is a last chorus of praise.* TSEIN *breaks through the crowd, just before the* EMPEROR *reaches exit.*)

TSEIN

Merciful emperor! Your weavers pray to you!

EMPEROR

What is your prayer?

TSEIN

Only let us remain in the houses, and weave on the looms of our ancestors.

EMPEROR

Remain in the houses and worship at the shrines of your ancestors. These men shall teach you their secrets. You and your children shall weave for the emperor in his city, forever. (*The weavers cry out in joy, some sobbing, some throwing up their hands.*) I know you are fit to be the royal weavers. If you were not, you would not have seen the beauty of my robes.

(*The weavers fall silent, suddenly.* TSEIN *springs after the* EMPEROR *as he turns to go. Confession is on her lips.* ZAN *leaps to cover her mouth with his hand, drawing her back. The* EMPEROR *passes on, not having seen the pantomime.*)

ZAN

Sh-h-h-h!

(*At the same moment the* CHILD *runs out from her doorway and rushes to* TSEIN. *She stops, gaping at the sight of the* EMPEROR, *and points speechlessly at him as he goes off. Her voice comes just as he disappears.*)

CHILD

Mother! The emperor has nothing on but a shirt!

(ZAR *puts a hand over her mouth and draws her into the crowd. The* CHILD *still points, unable to speak. The* EMPEROR'S *music is dying away. The weavers look at each other.*)

LING.

(*To* MONG.) Did you see anything?

MONG

(*Looking at the* CHILD.) No ——

TSEIN

(*Overwhelmed.*) There was nothing.

ROGUES

Sh-h-h-h-h-h ——

(*Rogues, fingers on lips, looking after the* EMPEROR'S *procession. As the music dies quite away, they begin to laugh, secretly, softly. The weavers slowly take in the joke, one at a time. They join the laughter. It grows and grows till the stage rocks with it.*)

ZAN

(*Above the laughter.*) Oh-h-h! This was a glorious adventure!

ZAR

But it is over! When the emperor finds out! (*Sign of beheading.*)

ZAN

Zar! We must get far from this place!

ZAR

Zan! We must never stop running till the milky way is winking at us through the dark!

ZAN

(*Leaping up to where they hid the treasure.*) Who wants gold and jewels?

ZAR

Gold for the emperor's new clothes!

ZAN

(*Flinging them about.*) Jewels for the emperor's tunics! Rubies! Emeralds!

ZAR

(*Also flinging them.*) Turquoise! Opals! Jade!

BOTH

Hold out your hands!

ZAN

(*Stripping off his rich coat.*) Who wants rich robes?

ZAR

Who wants glittering shoes?!

BOTH

(*Flinging fine garments and shoes.*) Catch! Catch!

ZAN

(*Leaping to exit, at the top of the steps.*) We are off!

ZAR

(*Following.*) We will go somewhere high up, and look down on many cities!

ZAN

We will choose the one where people are most foolish!

ZAR

There we will have our next adventure!

BOTH

(*As they leap out of sight.*) Ah-h-h-ha!

CURTAIN

HANSEL and GRETEL

by LILLIAN and ROBERT MASTERS

FANTASY—3 ACTS

13 Characters—Scenes: the Woodcutter's Hut, the Forest, the Witch's House in the Forest

With a bare cupboard and no food forthcoming, the stepmother contrives to leave little Hansel and Gretel deep in the woods, to shift for themselves. Their playmates set off in search of them, but are captured by Witch Wicked and turned into a gingerbread fence. Hansel and Gretel are also caught, but outwit the witch and break her spell. The stepmother arrives remorseful, and all go home laded with baskets of jewels.

Price, $1.00. (*Royalty,* $15.00.)

PUSS IN BOOTS

by ROWENA BENNETT

FANTASY—3 ACTS

12 Characters—Scenes: a Mill Exterior, a Forest Road, a Castle Exterior

A most excellent dramatization of the old fairy tale, which premiered at the Goodman Memorial Theatre, Art Institute of Chicago. Puss acquires the magical boots of the ogre, and with them cleverly plots to bring about a meeting between his master and a beautiful princess who is traveling through the land. He outwits the fiendish ogre, breaks the spell upon the castle and those within, delivers the palace to his master, and prepares for the royal wedding.

Price, $1.00. (*Royalty,* $15.00.)

Recent

Children's Plays

The Enchanted Journey

Go Jump In the Lake

The Golden Grotto

Gowain and the Green Knight

Harkee the Cat

The Invention

Korczak and the Children

Leroy and the Ark

The Lion Who Wouldn't

New Lamps for Old

The Owl and the Pussycat Went to See

Rocco, the Rolling Stone

The Tiger in Traction

The Thwarting of Baron Bollingrew

The Wise Men and the Elephant

Printed in U.S.A. #144